Graphing

GRADE 1

Written by Catherine Hernandez

Illustrated by Becky Radtke

Cover Illustration by Susan Cumbow

FS112035 Graphing Grade 1

23740 Hawthorne Blvd.
Torrance, CA 90505

TABLE OF CONTENTS

INTRODUCTION

This book has been designed to help students succeed in math. It is part of the *Math Minders* series that provides students with opportunities to practice math skills that they will use throughout their lives.

This book provides a variety of graphing activities. These activities will help children learn how to understand and interpret graphs. Interpreting graphs is "real math" and helps children develop higher level thinking skills.

The beginning activities help children understand that graphs present information of one kind or another. They also help children understand how to locate such information on a graph. The activities are based on topics familiar and interesting to children. After using an activity from this book, you may wish to have your students create their own graphs based on the same or a similar topic. This will enhance their understanding of the graphing process. This book is also appropriate for home learning.

The activities progress to include collecting data and interpreting graphs. These activities involve children in comparing and contrasting information presented on graphs, drawing conclusions, adding information in two columns, and more. The book includes picture graphs, horizontal bar graphs, and vertical bar graphs. The formats and question styles vary from page to page to help ensure that children become familiar and comfortable with graphing concepts.

Graphing

GRADE 1

Name ____________________

Going to School

Making a simple graph

Jake stood in front of the school and watched the kids arrive.

Count what Jake saw. Write the number.

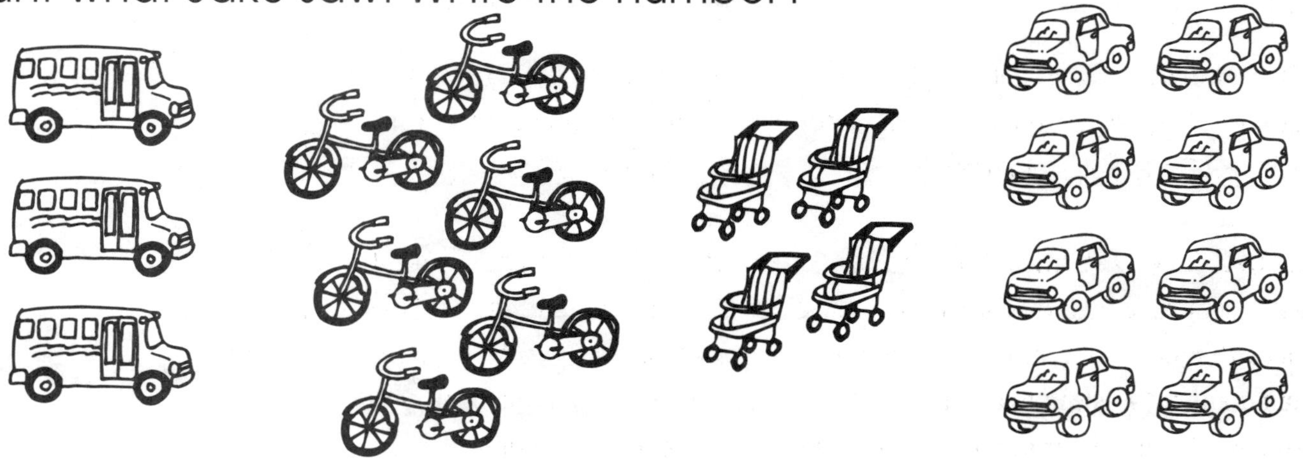

_______ _______ _______ _______

Color the graph to show how many.

(bus)								
(bicycle)								
(stroller)								
(car)								
	1	2	3	4	5	6	7	8

Name ____________________

All Kinds of Shoes

Reading a simple picture graph

The kids at school made a graph showing the different kinds of shoes they were wearing.

Kind of Shoes	Number of Kids Wearing Each Kind

Count to see how many kids were wearing each kind of shoe. Write the number.

Name ____________________

Apple Time

Reading a simple picture graph

Kate works at the Apple Store.
She made a graph to show what she sold on Monday.

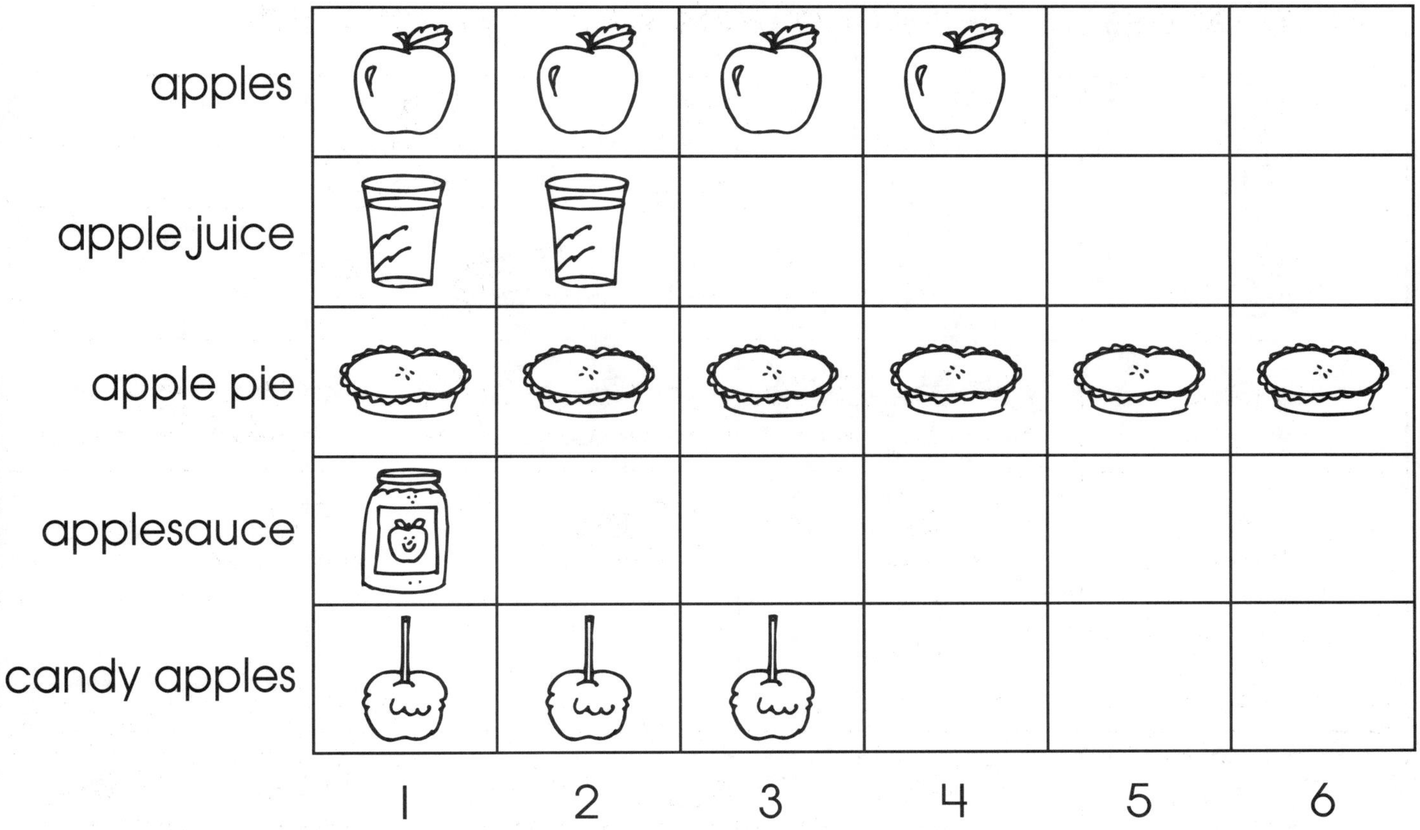

apples						
apple juice						
apple pie						
applesauce						
candy apples						
	1	2	3	4	5	6

How many did Kate sell? Write the number.

______ 

______ 

______ 

______ 

______ 

Circle the food that Kate sold most.

Name________________________________

Favorite Stories

Using tally marks/Making a graph

Mrs. Nice made a list of stories. Each child told which story was his or her favorite. Mrs. Nice made a tally mark for the story. A tally mark is a straight line.

Count the tally marks and write the number.

Color the boxes to show how many children chose each story.

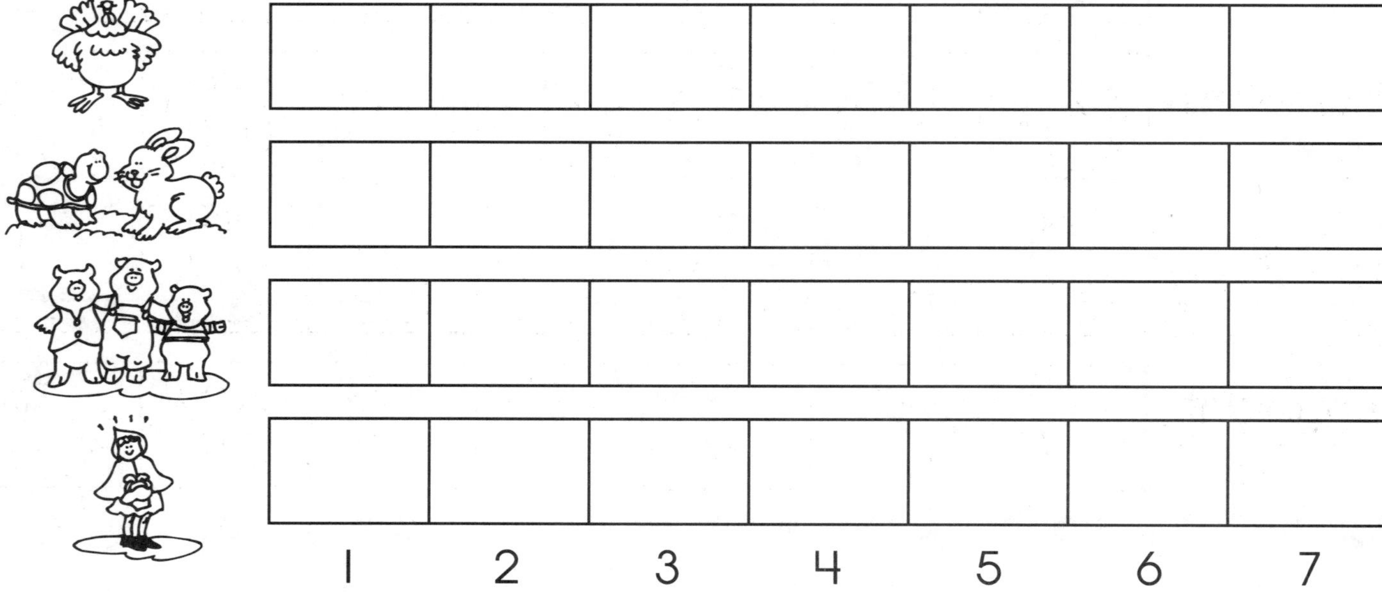

Name______________________________

Farmers Market

Making a graph

Kim bought fruits and vegetables for her family.
Color the graph to show how many she bought.

6 apples 

5 ears of corn 

7 potatoes 

2 pumpkins 

4 pears 

1 eggplant 

apples							
ears of corn	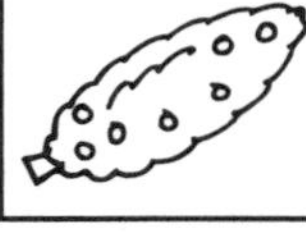		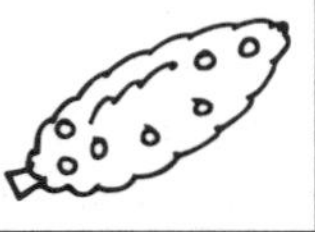	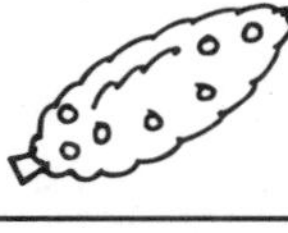	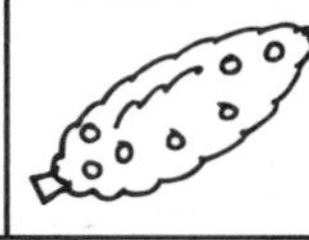	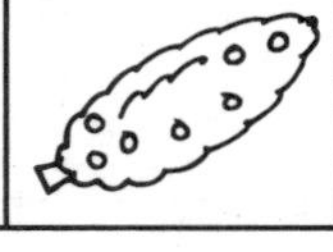	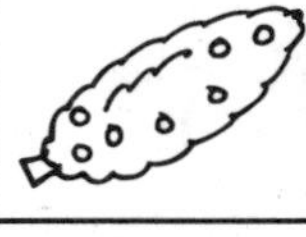
potatoes		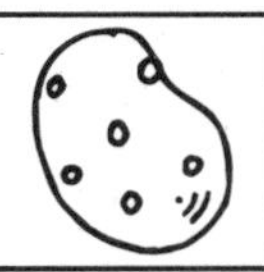	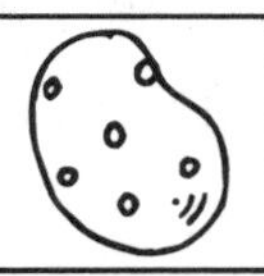	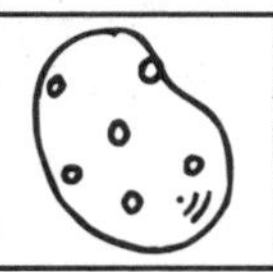		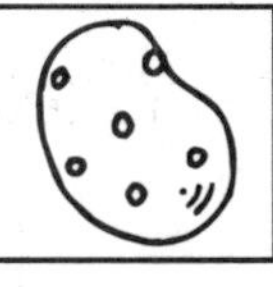	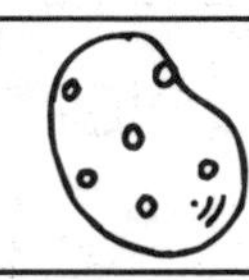
pumpkins							
pears	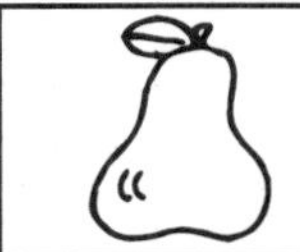						
eggplant				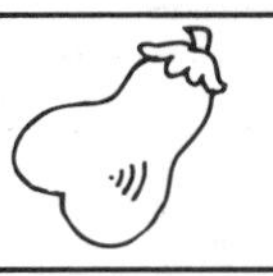			
	1	2	3	4	5	6	7

Name ____________________

Favorite Zoo Animals

Making a bar graph

Ask 10 people to choose a favorite zoo animal from this page. Make a tally mark to show the animal each person chose.

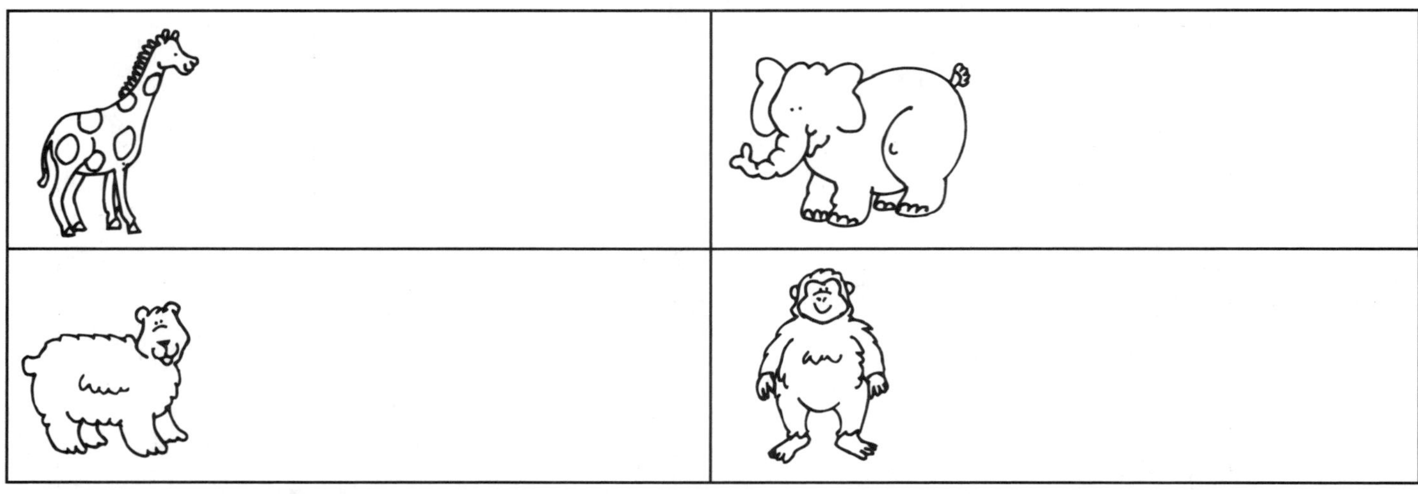

Color one box on the graph for each tally mark.

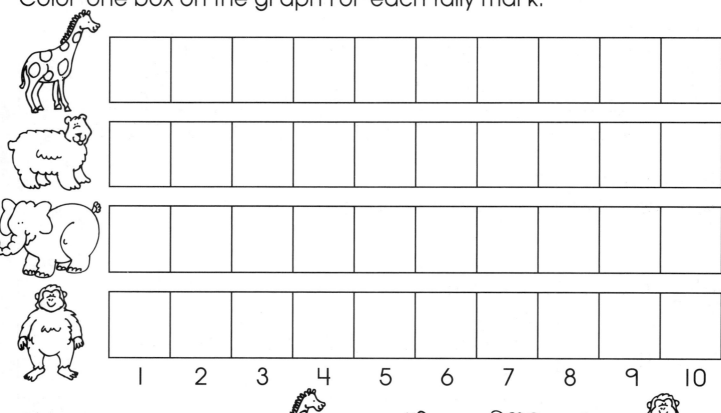

1	2	3	4	5	6	7	8	9	10

Circle the animal that is the favorite.

Name ______________________________

Helping Others

Reading a vertical picture graph

Mr. Pat asked the kids to bring cans and boxes of food to share with people who needed them.

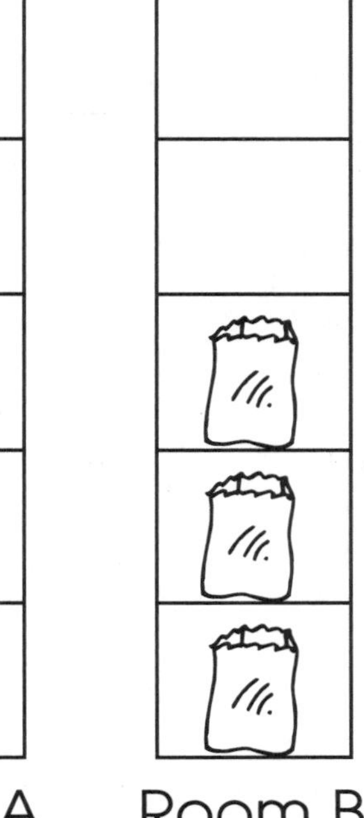
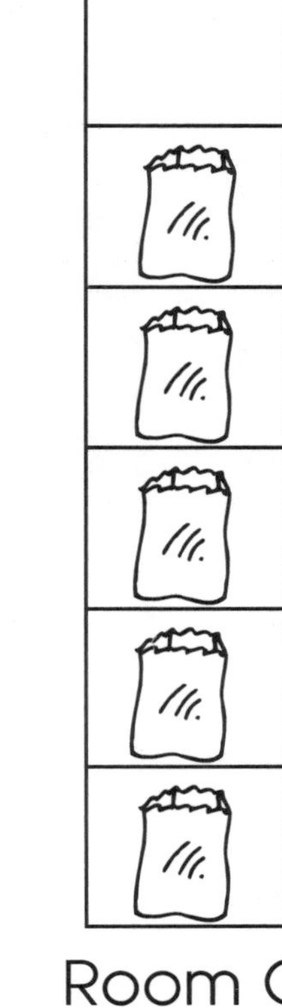
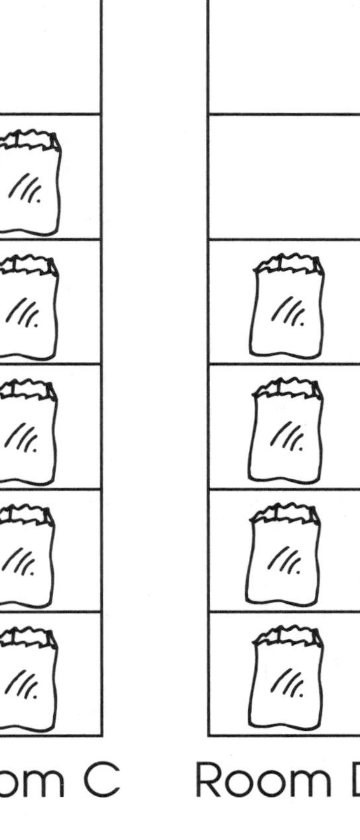

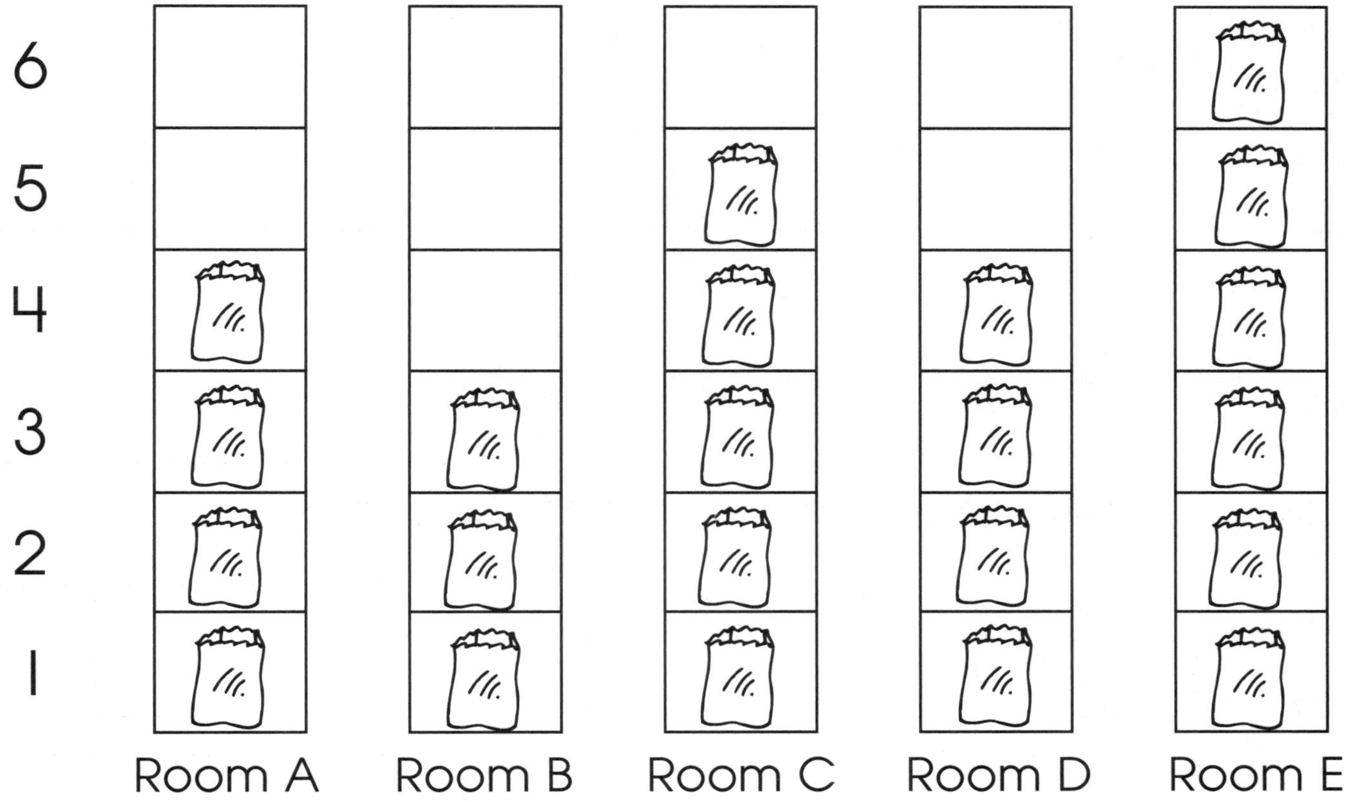

Read the graph.
How many bags of food did each room collect?

Room A ________ Room B ________ Room C ________

Room D ________ Room E ________

Which room collected the most bags? ________

Name ____

Winter Birds

Using a bar graph

Jon made a graph of the birds he saw at the feeder one day.

chickadee 

blue jay

cardinal

bobwhite 

woodpecker 

1 2 3 4 5 6 7

Use the graph to answer the questions.

A. How many  came? ________

B. How many  came? ________

C. How many  came? ________

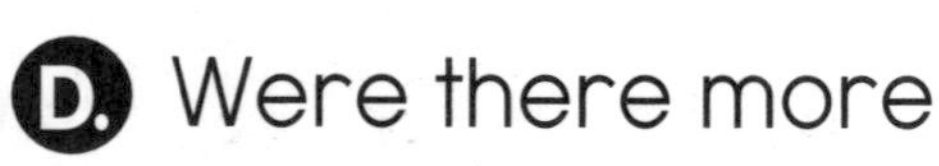

D. Were there more  than  ? yes no

E. Were there more  than  ? yes no

Name____

The Toy Makers

Reading a picture graph

This graph shows how many toys each worker made.

Worker	Number of Toys								

How many toys did the worker make?

____

____

____

____

Who made more? Circle the picture.

Name ____________________

Fun in the Snow

Reading a bar graph

The kids were asked "What is your favorite snow activity?" They made a graph to show their answers.

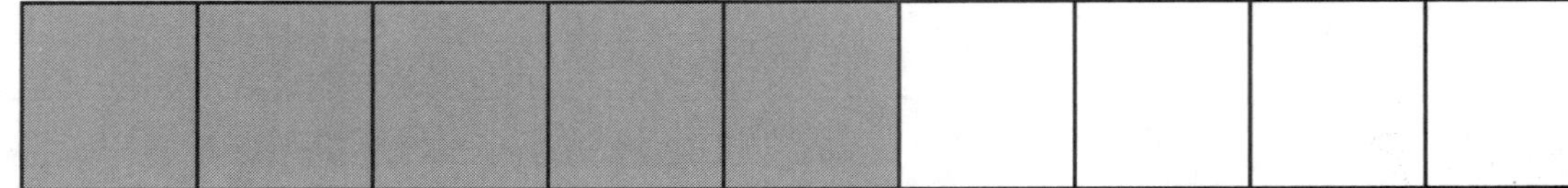

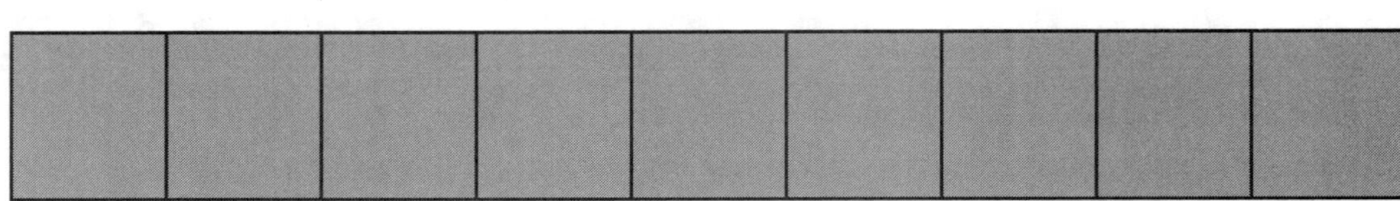

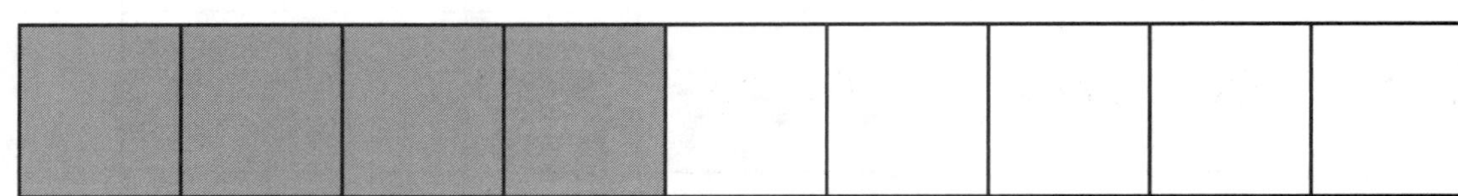

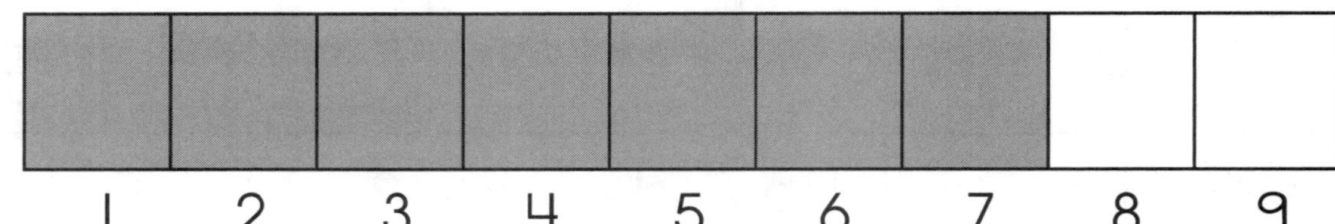

A. Which activity did the most kids choose?

B. Which activity did the fewest kids choose?

C. Which activity do you like best?

Name ______________________________

Weather Ways

Using tally marks/Making a bar graph

Ask 10 people to choose their favorite kind of weather.
Make a tally mark to show the kind of weather each person chose.

 ____________________  ____________________

____________________  ____________________

Color one box on the graph for each tally mark.

1	2	3	4	5	6	7	8	9	10

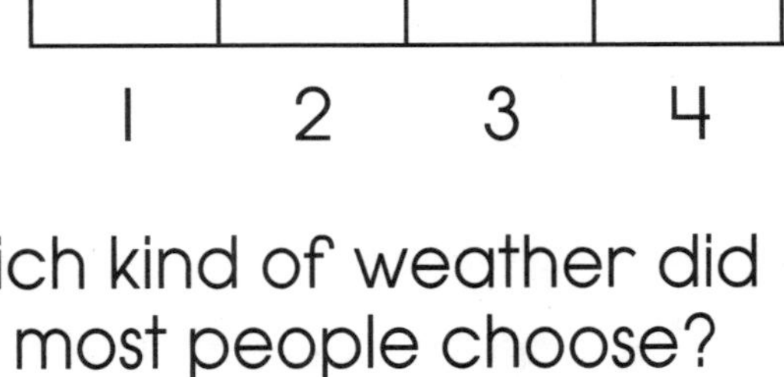

A. Which kind of weather did the most people choose?

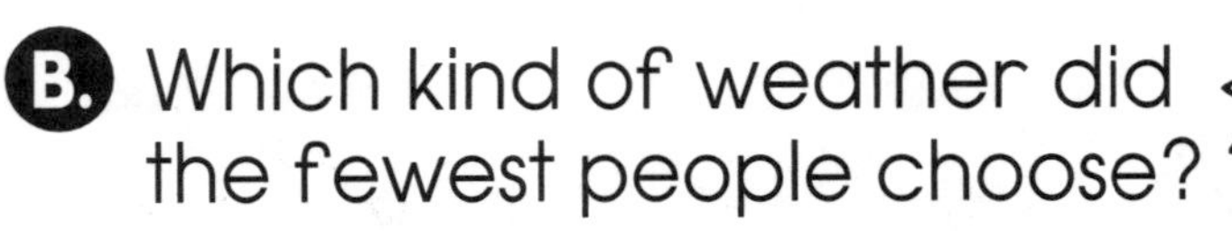

B. Which kind of weather did the fewest people choose?

  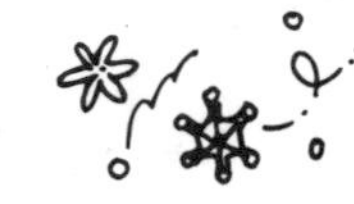

Name____

Pizza Time

Using a bar graph to solve problems

Pizza Pete made a graph to show the different kinds of pizza he sold one Saturday night.

Use the graph to answer the questions.

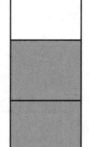

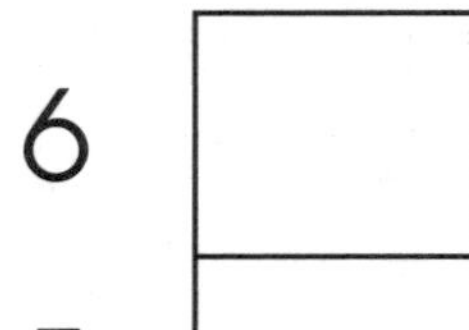
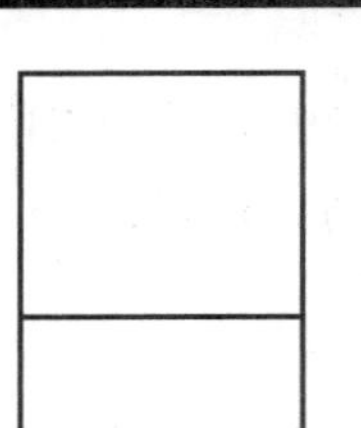

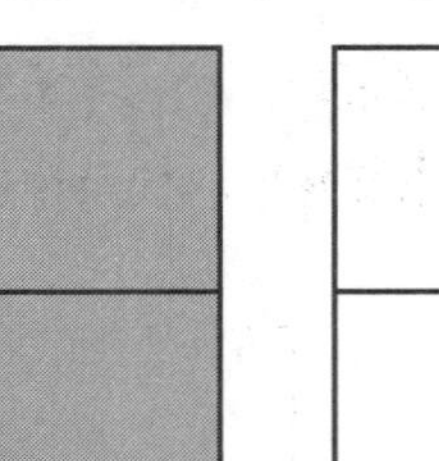

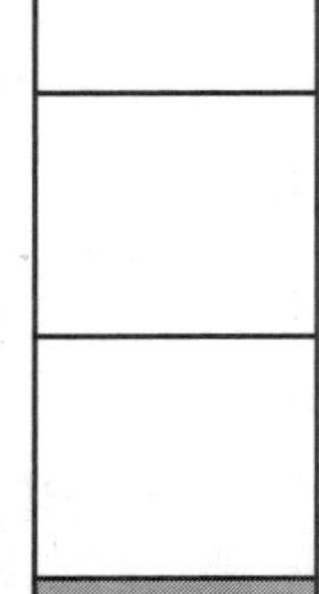
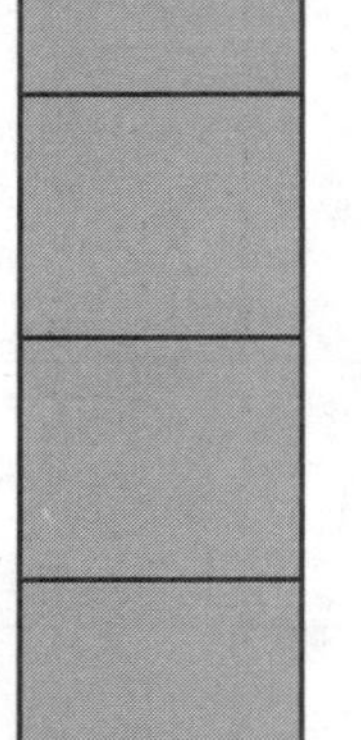

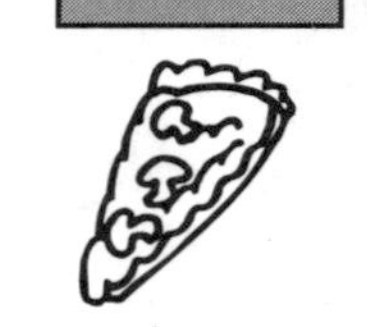

A. How many  were sold? __________

B. How many  were sold? __________

C. How many  and  were sold in all? __________

D. How many  and  were sold in all? __________

Name ________________________________

Computer Time

Reading a picture graph

The kids made a graph to show how many hours they spent working on the computer during one month.

	Jon	Amy	Luke	Cam	Jill
6					
5					
4					
3					
2					
1					

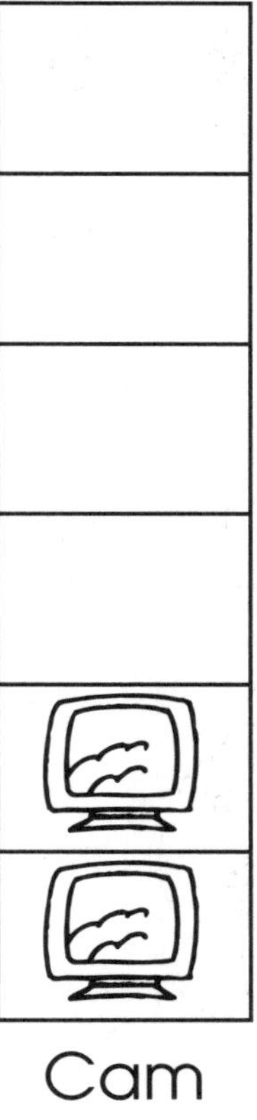

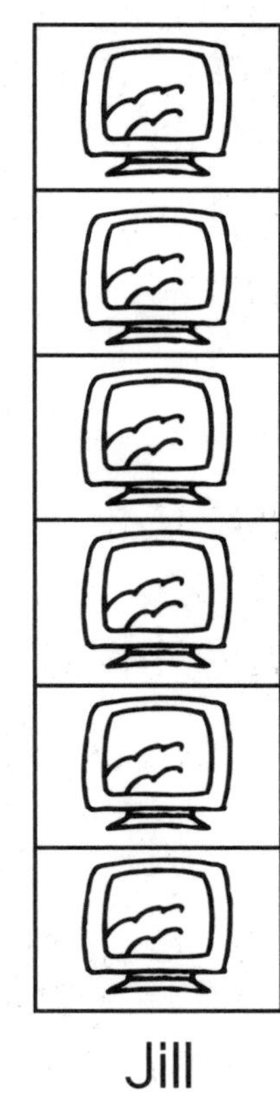

How many hours did each child spend on the computer?

Jon ________ Amy ________ Luke ________ Cam ________ Jill ________

Who spent more time on the computer?

 Jon or  Luke

B. Luke or Jill

Who spent less time on the computer?

 Amy  or Jill

 Cam or Jon

Name ____

A New Chimp Home

Reading a vertical bar graph

The chimps have a new home at the zoo. It is like their home in the forest.

This graph shows how many classes came to see the chimps each day.

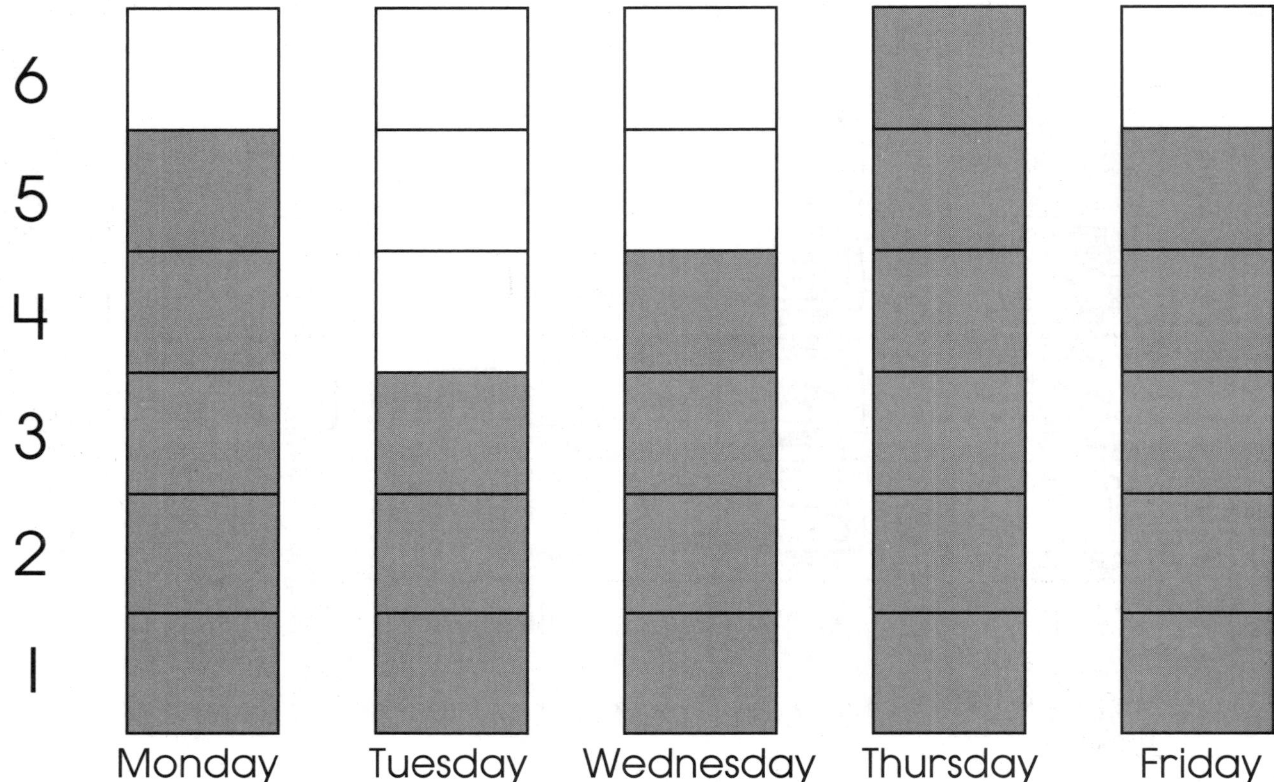

A. How many classes came on Monday? ________

B. How many classes came on Wednesday? ________

C. What day did the most classes come? ____________________

D. What day did the fewest classes come? ____________________

Name ____________________

Ways to Go

Reading a bar graph

Jeff made a list of special ways he has traveled. Then he made a graph showing the number of times he has traveled each way.

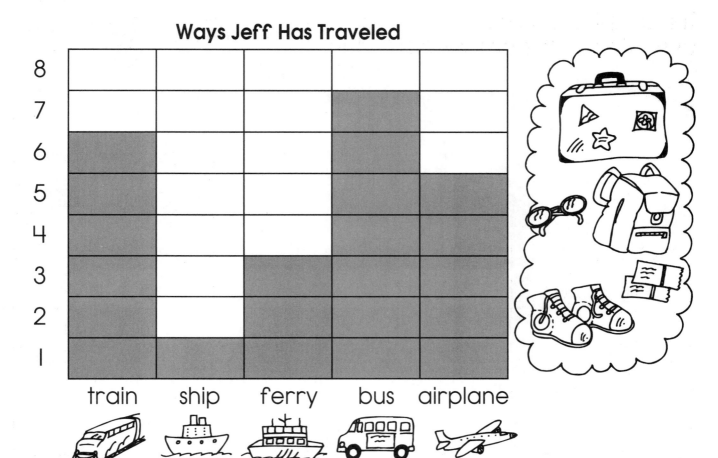

Ways Jeff Has Traveled

8
7
6
5
4
3
2
1

train ship ferry bus airplane

A. How many times has Jeff been on a ferry? ________

B. What way has Jeff traveled most often? ________

C. How many times has Jeff been on an airplane? ________

D. What way has Jeff traveled least often? ________

E. How many times has Jeff been on a train? ________

Name ____________________

At the River

Reading a bar graph

The Brown family went for a walk along the river. This graph shows the animals they saw.

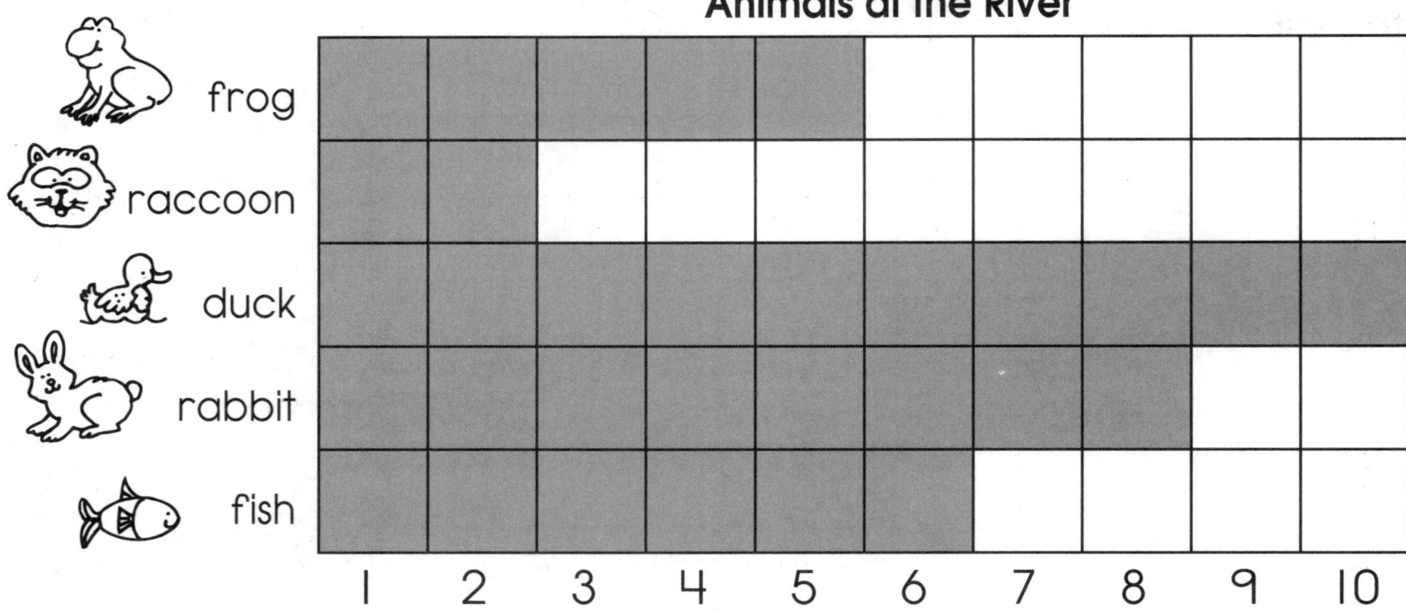

How many of each animal did the Brown family see?

frog ____ raccoon ____ duck ____ rabbit ____ fish ____

A. How many more  than  ? ________

B. How many more  than  ? ________

C. How many more  than  ? ________

D. How many  and  in all? ________

Name ____

Fly a Kite

Making a picture graph

Lots of people were flying kites at the park.

Color the graph to show the different kinds of kites.

Number of Kites at the Park

5	9	7

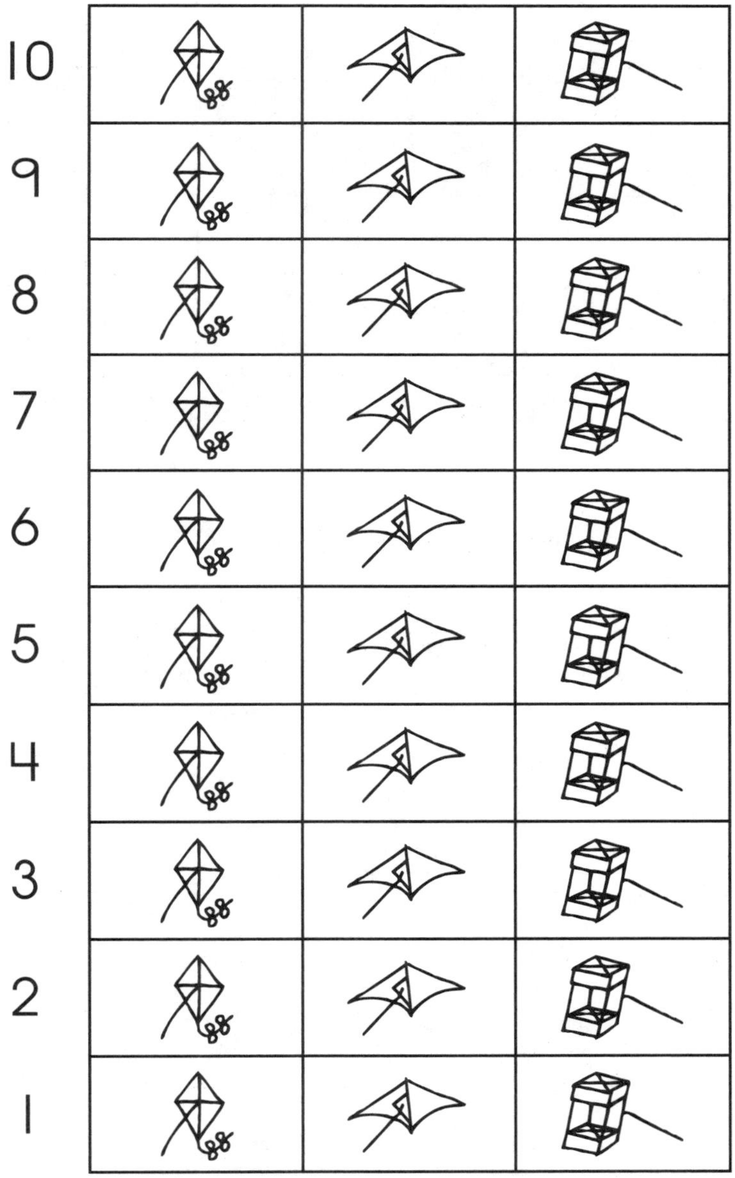

10			
9			
8			
7			
6			
5			
4			
3			
2			
1			

Circle the picture to answer the question.

A. What kind of kite was most common?

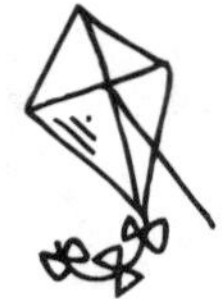  

B. What kind of kite was least common?

C. Which of these two kites was more common?

Name ______________________________

Time for Recess

Reading a bar graph

Mrs. White asked her students "What is your favorite recess activity?" The students made a graph to show their answers.

Favorite Recess Activities

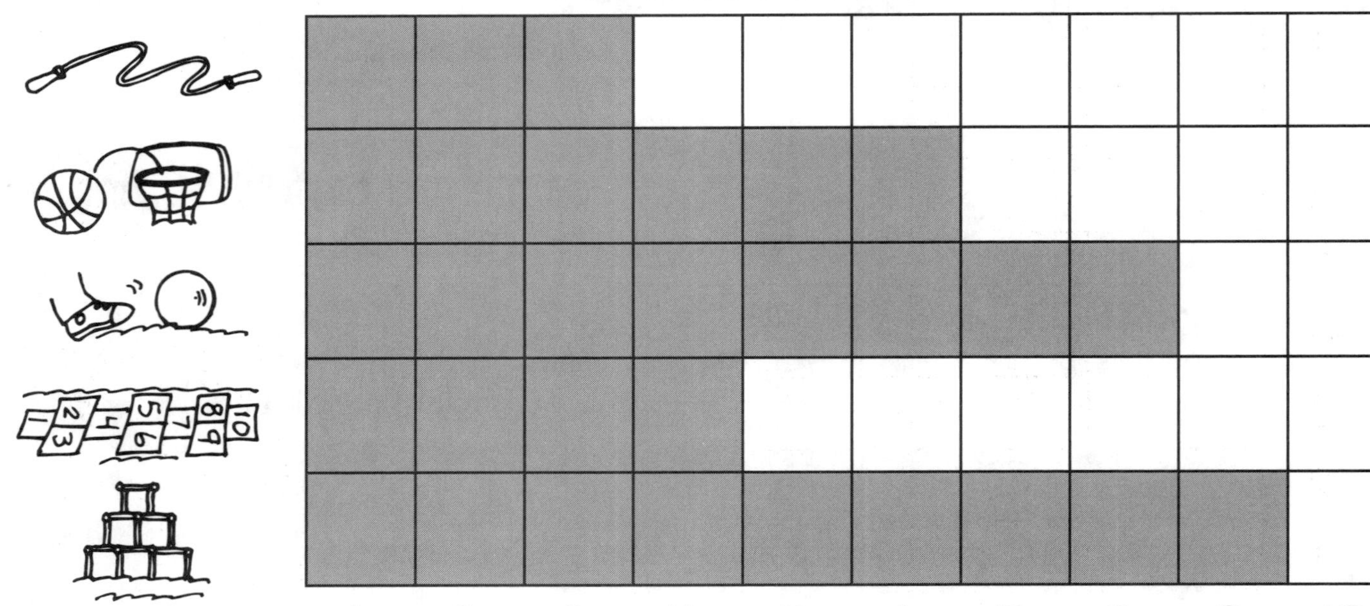

Circle the picture to answer the question.

A. Which activity did the most kids choose?

B. Which activity did the fewest kids choose?

C. Which of these activities did more kids choose?

D. Which of these activities did fewer kids choose?

Name ____

Arts and Crafts

Reading a bar graph

At summer camp, the kids in Cabin A made crafts every day. This graph shows what they made in one week.

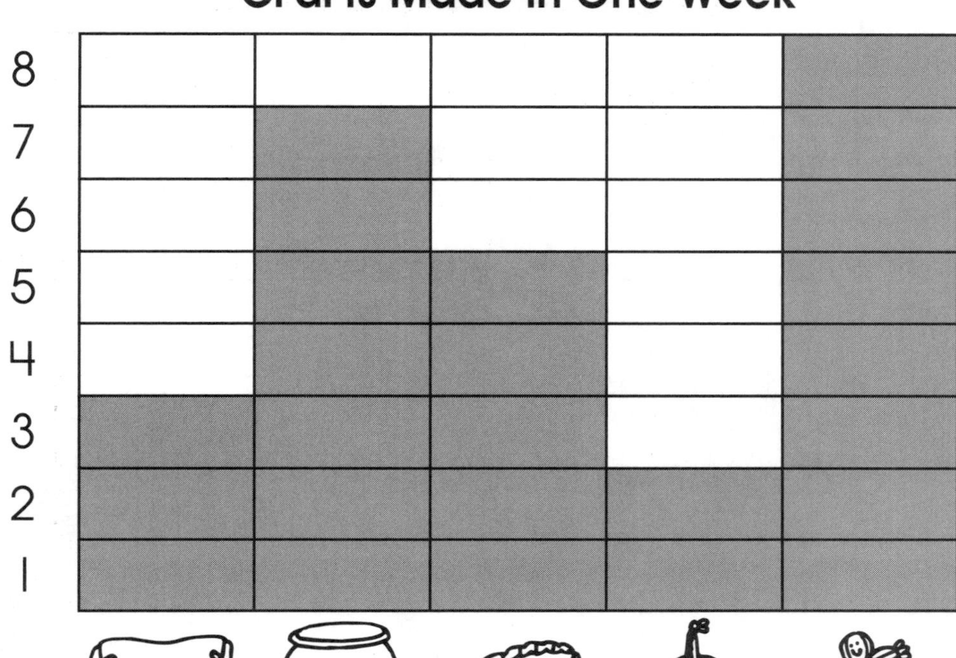

A. How many more  than  ? __________

B. Were more  made than  ? __________

C. How many  were made ? __________

D. How many  were made ? __________

E. Were fewer  made than  ? __________

Name ____________________

Places to Go

Making a bar graph

Ask 10 people to choose a favorite place to visit from this page. Make a tally mark to show the place each person chose.

movie theater ____________

fun theme park ____________

beach or lake ____________

shopping mall ____________

Color one box on the graph for each tally mark.

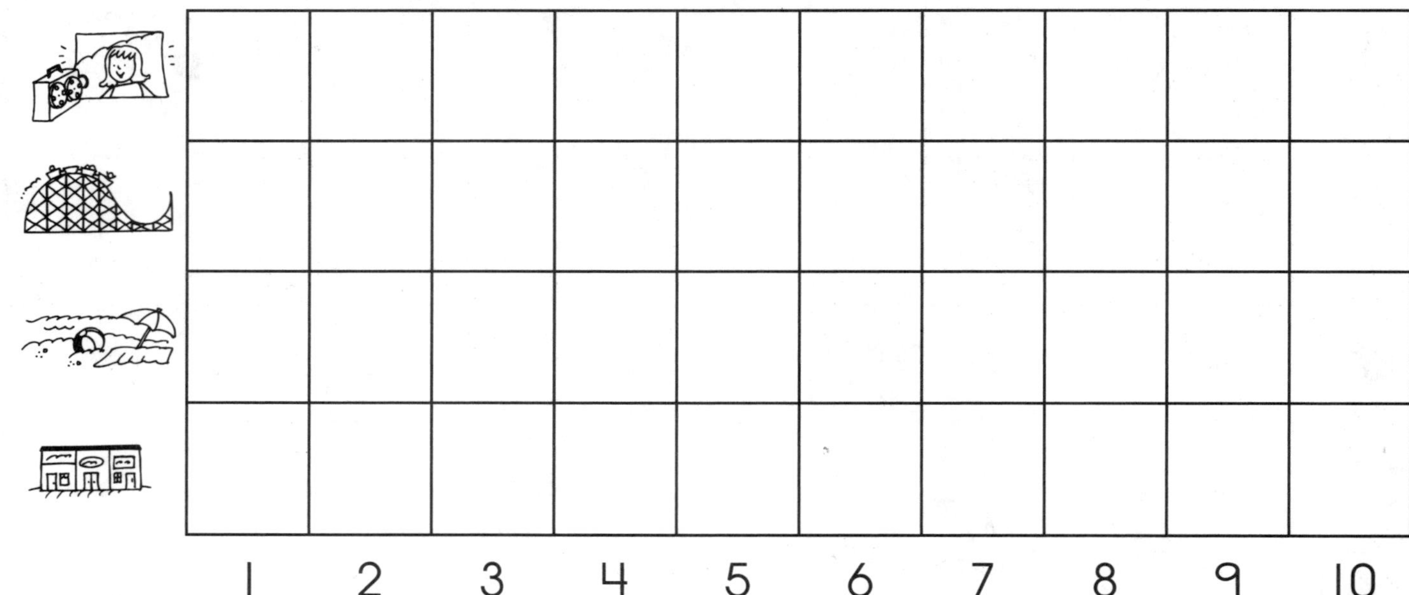

A. Which place is the most popular? ____________

B. Which place is the least popular? ____________

Name ____________________

Hatching Chicks

Reading a picture graph

At the Science Center, eggs are kept warm in a special glass case. People can watch as chicks hatch from the eggs.

This graph shows how many chicks hatched in one week.

Chicks That Hatched In One Week

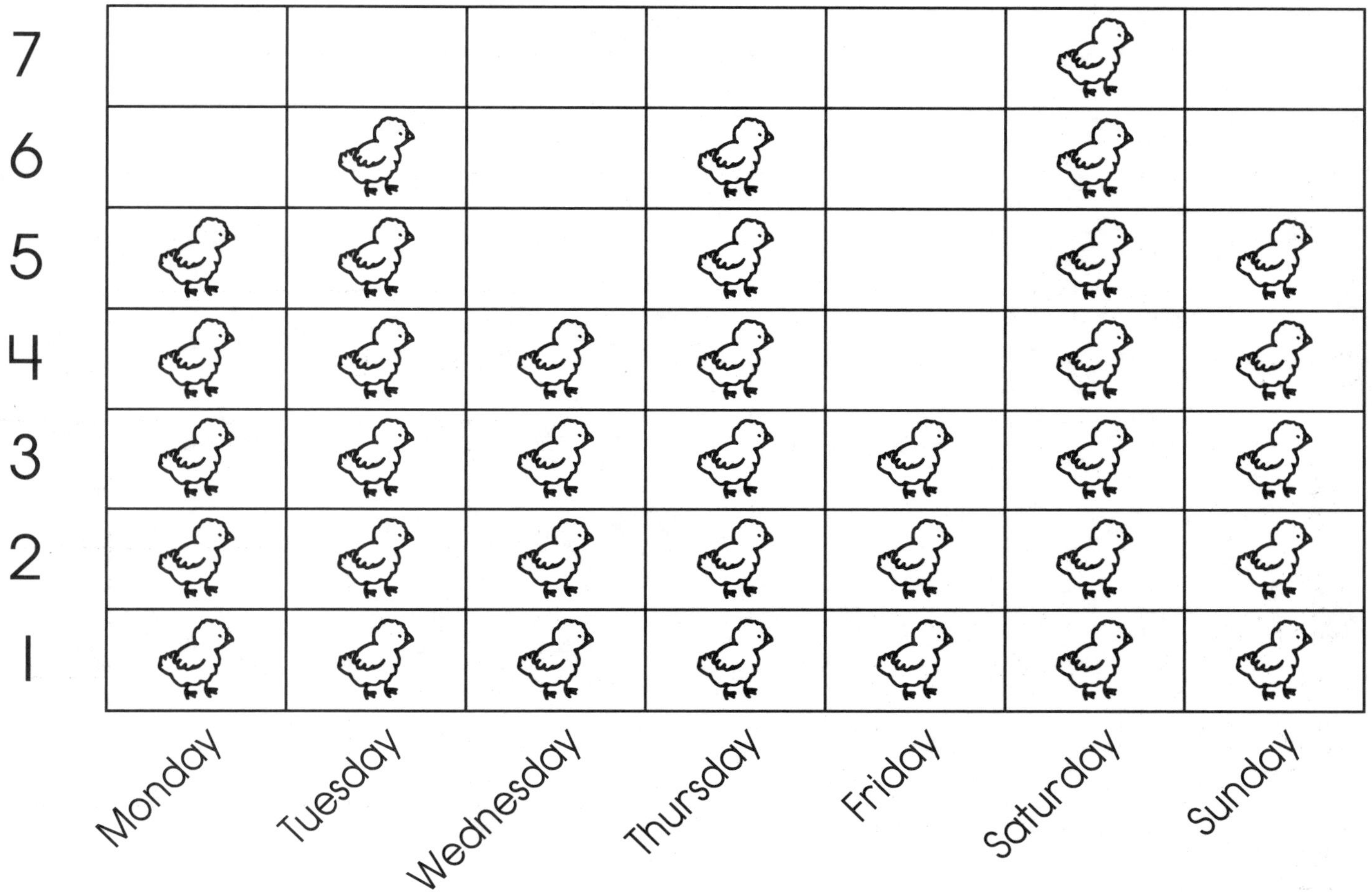

7
6
5
4
3
2
1

Monday Tuesday Wednesday Thursday Friday Saturday Sunday

A. How many chicks hatched on Tuesday? ________

B. On what day did the most chicks hatch? ________

C. On what day did 4 chicks hatch? ________________

D. How many chicks hatched on the weekend? ________________

Name ____________________

Busy Helpers

Reading a picture graph

Hannah and her friends helped out at the library. They made bookmarks to give away to other kids.

This graph shows how many bookmarks they made.

Bookmarks Made By Hannah and Her Friends

7					
6					
5					
4					
3					
2					
1					
	Hannah	Jason	Jenny	Matt	Kate

How many bookmarks did each child make?

Hannah	Jason	Jenny	Matt	Kate
______	______	______	______	______

Who made more?

A. Jason or Jenny 

B. Hannah or Kate

Who made less?

C. Matt or Jason

D. Jason or Kate

Name ______________________________

Shell Collection

Reading a bar graph

Nick has a shell collection. Each summer he visits the beach and adds to his collection.

This graph shows how many shells Nick has in his collection.

Nick's Shell Collection

A. How many more  than  ? __________

B. How many  and  are there in all? __________

C. How many  does Nick have? __________

D. Does Nick have fewer  than  ? __________

E. How many  and  are there in all? __________

F. Does Nick have more  than  ? __________

Name ______________________________

Flowers for Workers

Reading a bar graph

The parents had a dinner to thank all the school workers. Each person who came got to choose one flower to take home.

This graph shows the number of flowers people chose.

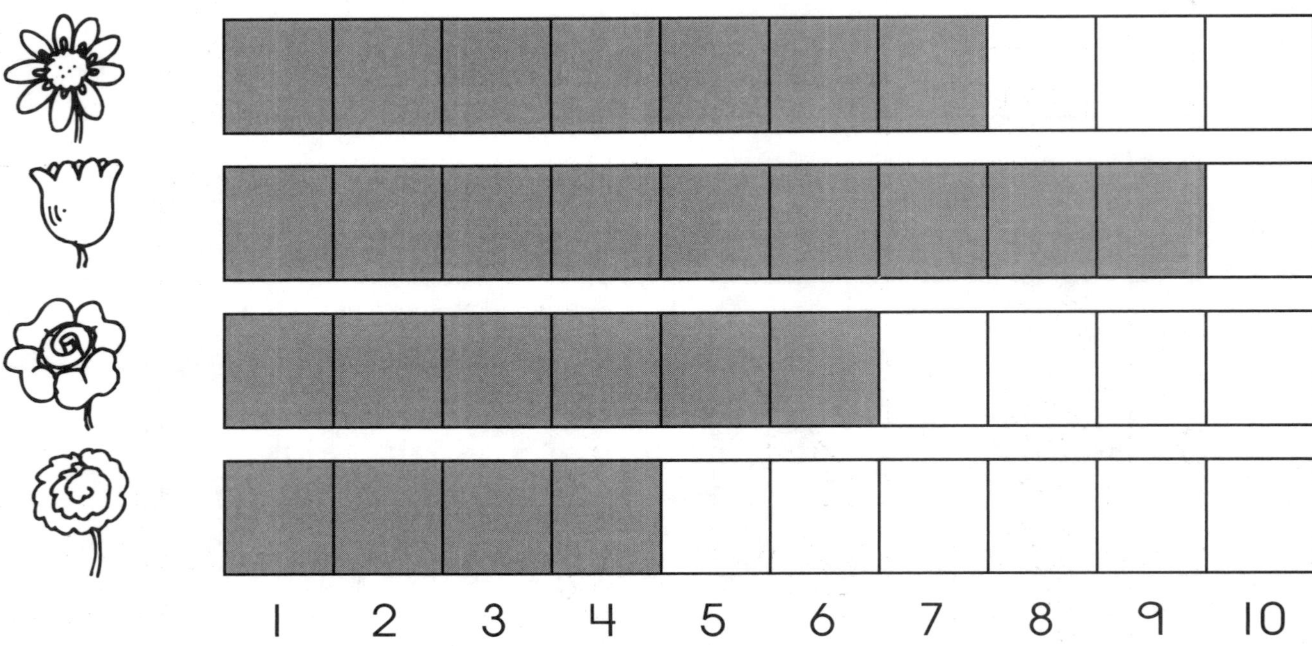

Circle the picture to answer the question.

A. Which kind of flower was chosen most often?

B. Which kind of flower was chosen least often?

C. Which of these flowers did more people choose?

D. Which of these flowers did fewer people choose?

Name ____

Button, Button

Reading a vertical bar graph

Cam likes to save buttons. She sorted her buttons and put them in lines to make a "button" graph.

7			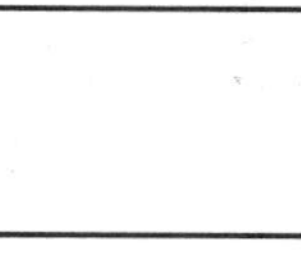	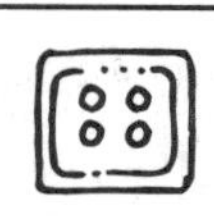	
6					
5				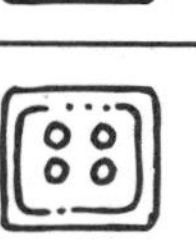	
4				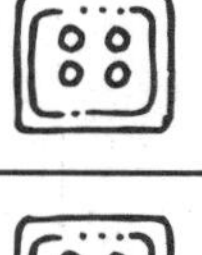	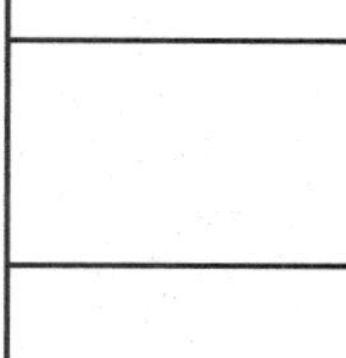
3					
2				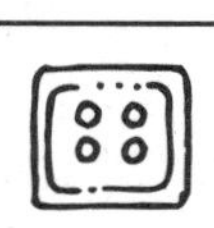	
1					

A. How many buttons? ________

B. How many more  than  ? ________

C. How many fewer  than  ? ________

D. How many  and  are there in all? ________

E. How many  and  are there in all? ________

Name ____________________

Save Those Cans!

Reading a bar graph

This graph shows how many cans were collected for recycling.

On this graph, one picture of a can equals two cans collected. Count by twos to find out how many cans each child collected.

= 2 cans

Aluminum Cans Collected

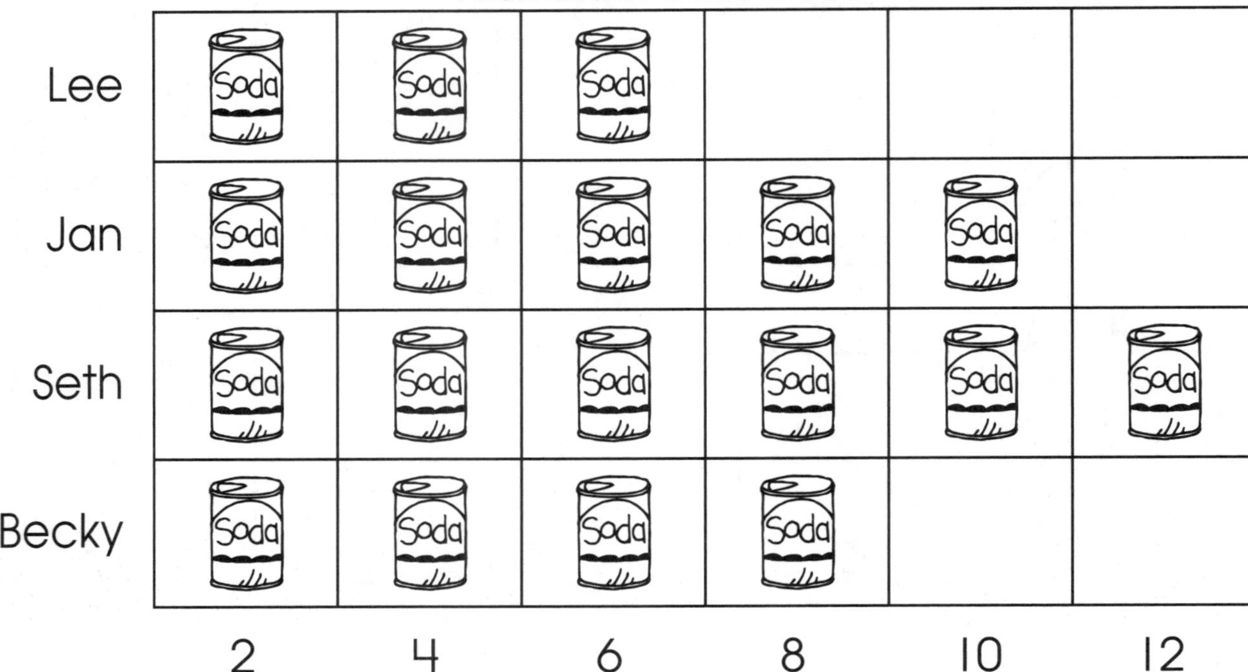

How many cans did each child collect?

Lee ________ Jan ________ Seth ________ Becky ________

Who collected more?

A. Lee or  Jan

B. Seth or Becky

Who collected less?

C. Jan or Seth

D. Becky or Lee

Name____

Coin Count

Making a vertical bar graph

Joy took all the coins out of her piggy bank.

Color the graph to show the coins that were in her bank.

Number of Coins in the Bank

5 pennies

8 nickels

6 dimes

pennies	nickels	dimes

A. Count by ones to find out how many cents the pennies are worth.

________ ¢

B. Count by fives to find out how many cents the nickels are worth.

________ ¢

C. Count by tens to find out how many cents the dimes are worth.

________ ¢

Name ____________________

My Own Graph

Making a bar graph

Use this page to make your own graph. You can think of your own idea or you can use one of these ideas:

The kind and number of pets in your neighborhood
The favorite kinds of ice cream of 10 people
The favorite colors of people in your neighborhood

10						
9						
8						
7						
6						
5						
4						
3						
2						
1						

ANSWERS

Page 3
buses—3
bikes—6
strollers—4
cars—8
Boxes on graph should be colored to match the above numbers.

Page 4
boots—3
sandals—4
tennis shoes—6
oxfords—3
dress shoes—1
loafers—5

Page 5
apples—4
apple juice—2
apple pies—6
applesauce—1
candy apples—3
The apple pie should be circled.

Page 6
The Little Red Hen—2
The Tortoise and the Hare—7
The Three Pigs—4
Red Riding Hood—3
Boxes on graph should be colored to match the above numbers.

Page 7
The following number of boxes should be colored in each row on the graph:
6 apples
5 ears of corn
7 potatoes
2 pumpkins
4 pears
1 eggplant

Page 8
Answers will vary but the number of boxes colored on the graph should match the tally marks for each animal.

Page 9
Room A—4
Room B—3
Room C—5
Room D—4
Room E—6
Room E collected the most bags.

Page 10
A. 2
B. 7
C. 5
D. no
E. yes

Page 11
A. 7
B. 6
C. 4
D. 9
E. Elf 1
F. Elf 4

Page 12
A. sledding
B. skating
C. Answers will vary.

Page 13
Answers will vary but the number of boxes colored on the graph should match the tally marks for each kind of weather.

Page 14
A. 1
B. 5
C. 11
D. 5

Page 15
Jon—3
Amy—4
Luke—5
Cam—2
Jill—6
A. Luke
B. Jill
C. Amy
D. Cam

Page 16
A. 5
B. 4
C. Thursday
D. Tuesday

Page 17
A. 3
B. bus
C. 5
D. ship
E. 6

Page 18
frog—5
raccoon—2
duck—10
rabbit—8
fish—6
A. 3
B. 2
C. 2
D. 7

ANSWERS

Page 19
The kites should be colored as follows:
First column—5
Second column—9
Third column—7
A. The middle kite should be circled.
B. The first kite should be circled.
C. The kite on the left should be circled.

Page 20
A. climbing bars
B. jump rope
C. basketball
D. hopscotch

Page 21
A. 4
B. no
C. 5
D. 3
E. yes

Page 22
Answers will vary but the number of boxes colored on the graph should match the tally marks for each place.

Page 23
A. 6
B. Saturday
C. Wednesday
D. 12

Page 24
Hannah—7
Jason—4
Jenny—5
Matt—6
Kate—5
A. Jenny
B. Hannah
C. Jason
D. Jason

Page 25
A. 2
B. 5
C. 1
D. no
E. 7
F. yes

Page 26
A. tulip
B. carnation
C. daisy
D. rose

Page 27
A. 7
B. 3
C. 3
D. 9
E. 7

Page 28
Lee—6
Jan—10
Seth—12
Becky—8
A. Jan
B. Seth
C. Jan
D. Lee

Page 29
A. 5¢
B. 40¢
C. 60¢